Basic Skills
SPELLING & PHONICS
for 6 – 7 year olds

Contents

Louis Fidge

Words ending with ll

FOCUS Lots of words end in ll.

bell

hill

TRY THESE

1. Write some ll words.

b	ill	bill
f	ill	
t	ill	

b	ell	
f	ell	
t	ell	

h	ill	
w	ell	
m	ill	
s	ell	

2. Finish these rhymes.

Jack and Jill went up the _____ .

Ding, dong, bell
Pussy's in the _____ .

Unit 1

3. Choose the right word for each picture.

| hill | fell | mill | yell |

__mill__   _____   _____   _____

4. Choose ill or ell to complete each word.

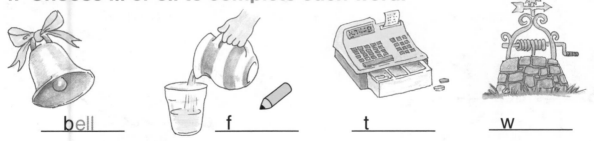

b__ell__   f____   t____   w____

 CHECK UP

5. Colour the ill words blue.   **Colour the ell words yellow.**

bell
mill   hill   will   fell
bill   pill   yell   fill   tell
sell   Jill   hill   till   well

Unit 1

Words ending in **ck**

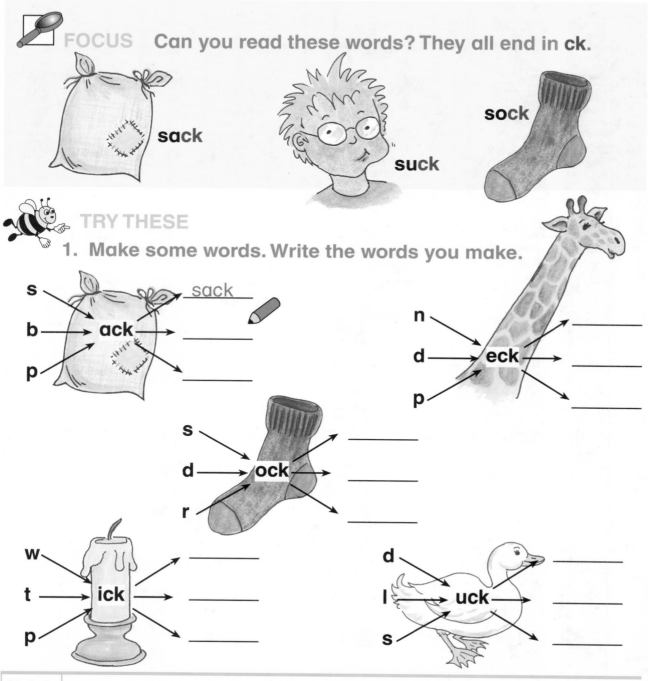

FOCUS Can you read these words? They all end in **ck**.

sack

suck

sock

TRY THESE

1. Make some words. Write the words you make.

s
b → **ack** → sack
p

_____
_____

n
d → **eck**
p

_____
_____
_____

s
d → **ock**
r

_____
_____
_____

w
t → **ick**
p

_____
_____
_____

d
l → **uck**
s

_____
_____
_____

2. Write the correct word under each picture.

| pack | peck | kick | lock | suck |

kick

_____

_____

_____

_____

3. Use the correct word in each sentence.

A bird can _peck._

You _____ a lolly.

You _____ a door.

You _____ a ball.

You _____ your bag.

 CHECK UP **4. Make the words.**

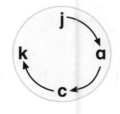

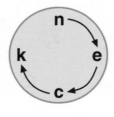

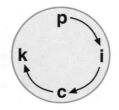

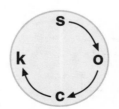

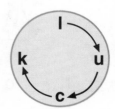

jack

_____

_____

_____

_____

Unit 2

Words with ee and oo

FOCUS

The sounds that birds and cows make will help you spell some words!

tweet

moo

TRY THESE 1. Make some words.
Write the words you make.

p__ee__l   f____l   h____l   p____p   k____p   d____p

peel   _____   _____   _____   _____   _____

p__oo__l   c____l   f____l   b____t   r____t   h____t

pool   _____   _____   _____   _____   _____

2. Write the correct word under each picture.

| boot | bee | pool | tree |

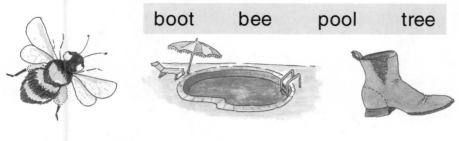

 bee   _____   _____   _____

3. Join the pairs of words that rhyme.   Write the words.

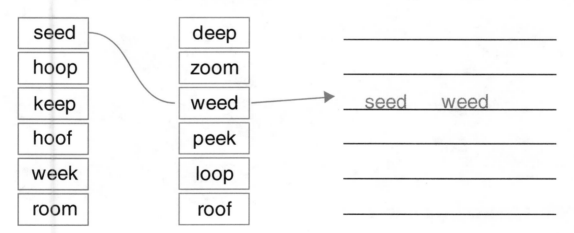

seed	deep
hoop	zoom
keep	weed
hoof	peek
week	loop
room	roof

_____

_____

 seed   weed

_____

_____

_____

4. Read the sentence. Complete each word with ee or oo.

You eat it.   f___d   Seven days.   w___k

It is on a house.   r___f   Part of a foot.   h___l

Words ending in **ng**

 **FOCUS**

There are three **ng** words in this sentence. Can you find them?

The king sang a song.

TRY THESE

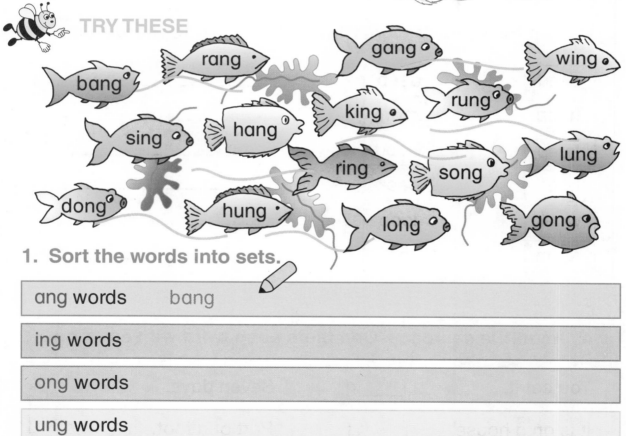

1. **Sort the words into sets.**

ang words	bang

ing words	

ong words	

ung words	

2. Choose the letter. Write the word.

a   o   i   u   o   a   u   o

g a ng   r   ng   b   ng   l   ng

<u>gang</u>

3. Look at each picture. Write the word.

a. sing

c. gong

b. wing

d. king

e. rung

f. ring

a.   sing

b.

c.

d.

e.

f.

4. Think of a rhyming word.

gang   ring   long   bung

<u>fang</u>

Words ending in **nd** and **nt**

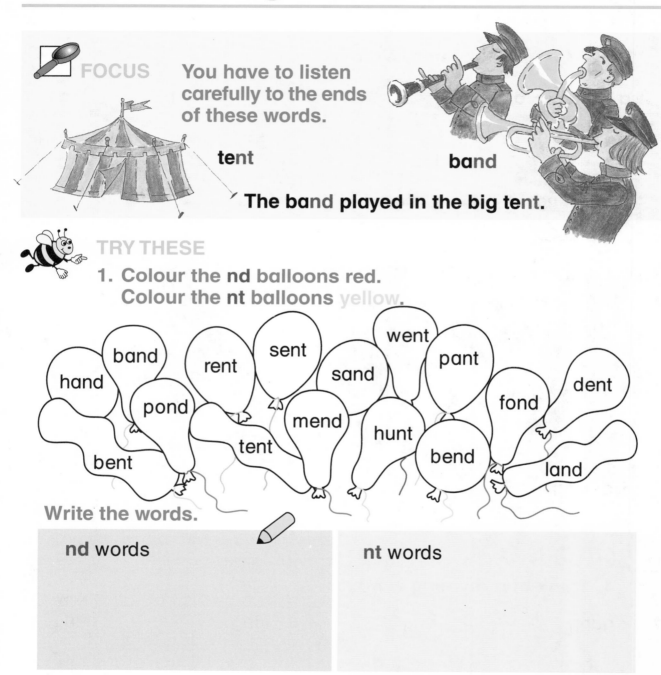

FOCUS You have to listen carefully to the ends of these words.

tent

band

The band played in the big tent.

TRY THESE

1. Colour the **nd** balloons red.
   Colour the **nt** balloons yellow.

hand · band · pond · bent · rent · tent · sent · mend · went · sand · hunt · pant · bend · fond · dent · land

Write the words.

nd words	**nt** words

2. Complete each word with **d** or **t**.

an <u>t</u>

<u>ant</u>

san __

_____

win __

_____

pon__

_____

ten__

_____

hun __

_____

3. Choose one of the words above to complete each sentence.

An <u>ant</u> is an insect.

A fox will _____ for food.

The _____ blows.

You can sleep in a _____.

I dig in the _____ .

A duck swims in a _____.

 CHECK UP

4. Find and circle the **nd** and **nt** words.

1. a b c d (h a n d) f g j

2. n m s b e n t y z x w

3. g f d s a l e n t y u p

4. f o n d q w e r t y u k

5. d w s x z a q m e n d

6. d x v b c z p a n t j l

Unit 5

Word beginnings

FOCUS

Look carefully at the
beginning of each of
these words.

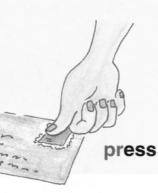

press

dress

TRY THESE   1. Make some words.

br ⌒ ick = _brick_

br ⌒ ing = _____

br ⌒ ag = _____

cr ⌒ ack = _____

cr ⌒ ust = _____

cr ⌒ op = _____

dr ⌒ ag = _____

dr ⌒ op = _____

dr ⌒ ip = _____

gr ⌒ ab = _____

gr ⌒ ip = _____

gr ⌒ uff = _____

pr ⌒ am = _____

pr ⌒ od = _____

pr ⌒ op = _____

tr ⌒ ap = _____

tr ⌒ uck = _____

tr ⌒ ip = _____

2. Choose the letters to complete the word.

br 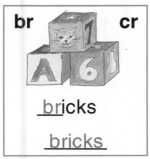 **cr**	**dr** 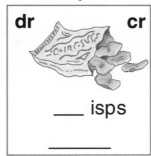 **cr**	**fr**  **dr**
<u>br</u>icks	___ isps	___ um
<u>bricks</u>	_____	_____
gr 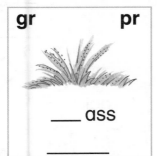 **pr**	**tr**  **pr**	**tr**  **br**
___ ass	___ am	___ uck
_____	_____	_____

3. Choose one of the words above to complete each sentence.

You drive a <u>truck</u> .   A baby goes in a _____ .

You bang a _____ .   A cow eats _____ .

You eat _____ .   A house is made with_____ .

 CHECK UP   4. Think of a word!

br<u>ing</u>   cr _____   dr_____

gr _____   pr _____   tr _____

1. Write the word. Draw the picture.

h ⟶ ill   t ⟶ ill   b ⟶ ell   w ⟶ ell

hill   _____   _____   _____

2. Colour the:

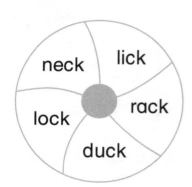

ack words red

eck words yellow

ock words orange

uck words green

ick words blue

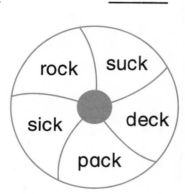

3. Complete these words with either **ee** or **oo**.

m____n   b____   tr____   p____l

4. Fill in the missing letter.

a   i

k __ ng

o   e

g __ ng

i   u

b __ ng

5. Write the nd words on the hand. Write the nt words on the tent.

went   bend   pond   tint   mend   hunt

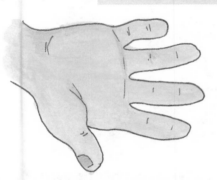

6. Use these beginnings and endings to make some words.

Beginnings	Endings	Some words I can make.
br	ick	brick
cr	uff	brag
dr	od	
gr	ag	
pr	op	
tr	ack	

Tricky word endings

There are many words that end with **l** and **another letter**. For example:

The elf had a gold belt.

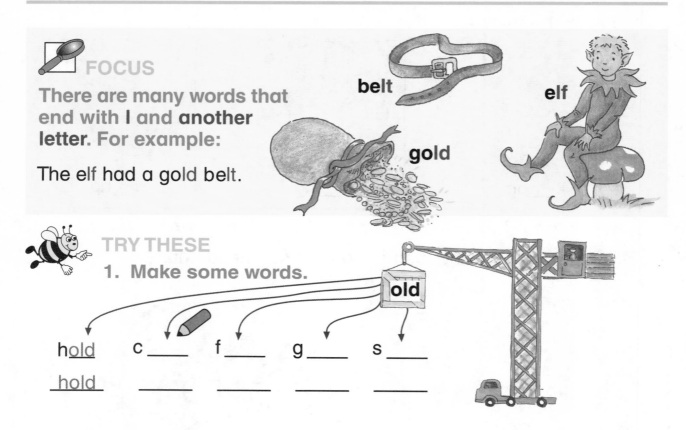

belt

elf

gold

TRY THESE

1. Make some words.

old

hold   c____   f____   g____   s____

hold   ____   ____   ____   ____

2. **Colour the lf words red.**   **Colour the lk words blue.**

Colour the lp words green.   **Colour the lt words yellow.**

sulk | belt | milk | help

elf | bolt | jolt | melt | shelf

yelp | golf | bulk | silk | felt

3. Write the correct word under each picture.

cold

help

milk

belt

elf

old

milk

_____

_____

_____

_____

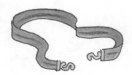

_____

4. Choose one of the words above to complete each sentence.

A <u>belt</u> keeps trousers up.

An _____ is a small person.

One day we will all get _____ .

I drink lots of _____ .

It is nice to _____ others.

In winter it is _____ .

5. Follow the lines. Work out the words.

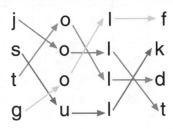

j o l f

s o l k

t o l d

g u l t

_____

_____

_____

jolt

Words with st

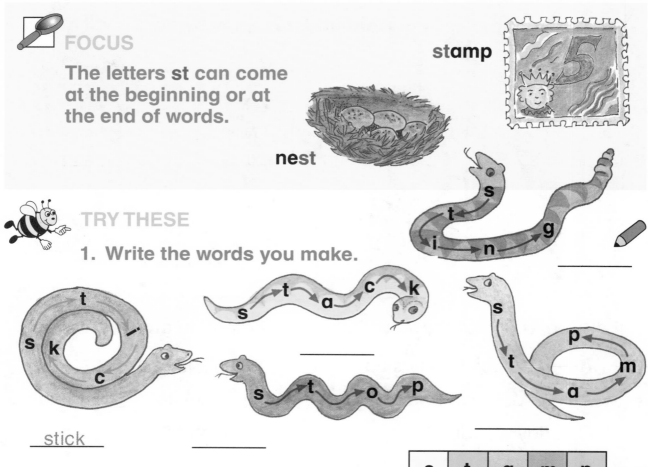

FOCUS

The letters **st** can come at the beginning or at the end of words.

stamp

nest

TRY THESE

1. Write the words you make.

__stick__

2. Use the words you have made.

You put this on a letter.

A bee does this.

This is made of wood.

To put boxes on top of each other

To stand still

s	t	a	m	p
s	t			
s	t			
s	t			
s	t			

Unit 8

3. Drive each car to the correct garage. Write the words.

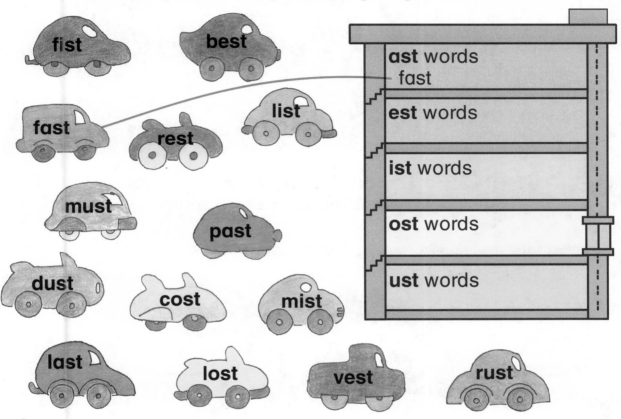

fist best list fast rest must past dust cost mist last lost vest rust

ast words
fast

est words

ist words

ost words

ust words

 CHECK UP

4. Draw a box around words with **st** at the beginning.

Circle the words with **st** at the end.

stiff pest stab stock test

rust stand past fist stuck

Unit 8

Words with sh and ch

FOCUS

The letters **ch** are like the sound you make when you sneeze!

achoo!

sh!

The letters **sh** make the quiet sound.

TRY THESE

1. **Add ch to make these words. Use the words you make.**

<u>ch</u>in ___ick ___imp ___eese ___ips ___air

a. <u>chick</u>

b. _____

c. _____

d. _____

e. _____

f. _____

2. **Find and circle the ch in these words.**

(ch)at   check   much   such

chop   rich   chocolate   church

MORE PRACTICE

3. Make these words.

<u>sh</u>ip   ___ell   ___eep   ___op   ___ut

<u>ship</u>   _____   _____   _____   _____

hu<u>sh</u>   wi___   cra___   ca___   fi___

<u>hush</u>   _____   _____   _____   _____

4. Use some of the words above.

It can swim.

A snail has one.

Another name for money.

You buy things in it.

When two things hit each other.

f	i	s	h		
		s	h		
		s	h		
		s	h		
		s	h		

 CHECK UP

5. Add ch or sh to make each word.

<u>ch</u>eck   ___ut   ___ill   ___ed   ___ild

___oot   lun___   da___   blu___   pin___

Unit 9

Words with **ar**

FOCUS These words all contain the same letter pattern. Can you spot it?

star

jar

car

TRY THESE

1. **Complete the words in the star with ar.**

   a. A metal rod   <u>bar</u>

   b. A long way away   _____

   c. Something you drive   _____

   d. It is made of glass.   _____

   e. It is put on roads.   _____

2. **Make the words.**

b + ark = <u>bark</u>
d + ark = _____
m + ark = _____
p + ark = _____
sh + ark = _____

3. Join the pairs of rhyming words. Write the words.

car	spark	_____
dart	darn	_____
barn	far	car far
lark	starch	_____
hard	charm	_____
farm	card	_____
march	part	_____

4. Write the correct word under each picture.

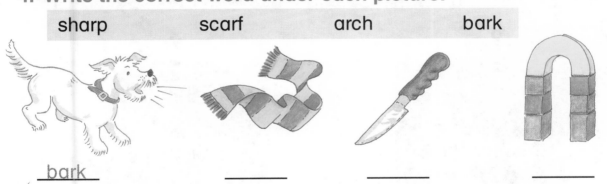

sharp	scarf	arch	bark

bark   _____   _____   _____

5. Match the beginning and ending of these words.   **Write the words.**

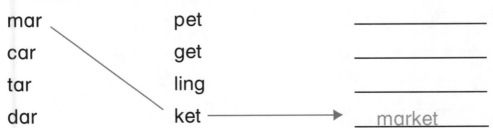

mar	pet	_____
car	get	_____
tar	ling	_____
dar	ket	market

Words with **ay**

 FOCUS

The letters **ay** often appear at the end of words.

Horses eat hay every day.

 TRY THESE

1. Write the words you can make with these **ay** machines.

b p h d m s

+ ay

may

cl st tr pr pl sw

+ ay

MORE PRACTICE

2. Finish each of the days of the week.

Fri<u>day</u>　　Tues _____

Mon _____　　Thurs _____

Sun _____　　Wednes_____

Satur _____

3. Now write the days in order.

<u>Sunday</u>

_____

_____

_____

_____

_____

_____

4. Use these ay words to answer the riddles.

| play | hay | tray | clay |

You carry things on me. <u>tray</u>

You make pots with me. _____

Horses eat me. _____

You do this for fun. _____

 CHECK UP　　**5. Find and circle the ay words.**

a b c d h (d a y) f g j　　　n m s a y n t y z x w

g f d s p l a y t y u p　　　s w a y q w e r t y u k

d w a y z a q m x n d　　　d x v b c z p r a y t l

Words within words

FOCUS If you look carefully you can often find small words in longer words.

Can you find cat in caterpillar?

Can you find ant in elephant?

TRY THESE **1. Find these animals in the words below.**

bat

ant

owl

duck

rat

otter

hen

ape

b(owl)

bath

when

ducked

spotter

rather

elephant

escape

2. Add a letter to these words and make the name of an animal.

_c_at   do__   __oat   sea__   came__   badge__

3. Find a small word in the name of each vegetable.

(pot)ato   carrot   onion   sprout   cauliflower   turnip

4. Circle the word that contains the small word.

all	read	(call)	open	jump
ink	teacher	two	goat	pink
and	band	sea	table	door
luck	funny	bang	cluck	bell
ring	bring	send	apple	book
arm	pencil	farmer	cart	bird
key	lion	gorilla	crocodile	monkey

CHECK UP   **5. How many small words can you find in these names?**

How many small words can you find in your name?

Matthew

mat the he

Bethany

_____

Progress check 2

1. Write the word. Draw the picture.

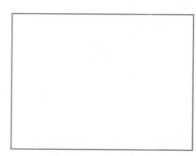

g + old

m + ilk

b + elt

___gold___

_____

_____

2. Colour the ast words red   est words yellow   ist words blue   ust words green   ost words orange

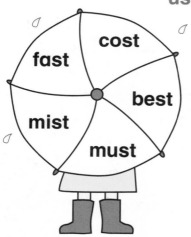

cost
fast
best
mist
must

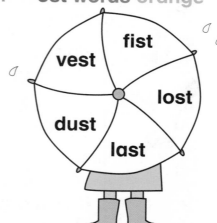

fist
vest
lost
dust
last

3. Complete these words with either sh or ch.

____ ick

____ eep

____ ips

____ ell

4. Write the words under the correct pictures.

| target | shark | farmer | jars |

_____   _____   _____   _____

5. Tick ✔ the real words.   Cross ✗ the nonsense words.

pay	✔	day	☐	vay	☐	zay	☐
way	☐	clay	☐	blay	☐	glay	☐
play	☐	tray	☐	kray	☐	sway	☐

6. Find and circle the animals hiding in these words.

s(cat)ter   then   boxing   grape

skids   stiffly   mother

been   feel   selfish   beard

Answers

Unit 1

1.   hill
   bill   bell   well
   fill   fell   mill
   till   tell   sell
2. hill   well
3. mill   yell   hill   fell
4. bell   fill   till   well
5. **ill** words - mill hill (× 2) will bill
   pill fill Jill till
   ell words - bell fell yell tell
   sell well

Unit 2

1. sack neck sock wick duck
   back deck dock tick luck
   pack peck rock pick suck
2. kick lock peck suck pack
3. peck   kick
   suck   pack
   lock
4. jack neck pick sock luck

Unit 3

1. peel   feel   heel
   peep   keep   deep
   pool   cool   fool
   boot   root   hoot
2. bee pool boot tree
3. keep – deep; room – zoom;
   seed – weed; week – peek;
   hoop – loop; hoof – roof
4. food   week
   roof   heel

Unit 4

1. bang rang gang hang
   wing sing king ring
   song dong gong long
   rung hung lung
2. gang ring bang long
3. a. sing b. wing c. gong
   d. king e. rung f. ring
4. There are many possible
   answers.

Unit 5

1. **nd** words - hand band pond
   mend sand bend fond land
   nt words - bent rent tent
   sent hunt went pant dent
2. ant   sand   wind
   pond   tent   hunt
3. ant   tent
   hunt   sand
   wind   pond
4. hand   bent
   lent   fond
   mend   pant

Unit 6

1. brick   crack
   bring   crust
   brag   crop
   drag   grab
   drop   grip
   drip   gruff
   pram   trap
   prod   truck
   prop   trip

Unit 6

2. bricks   crisps   drum
   grass   pram   truck
3. truck   pram
   drum   grass
   crisps   bricks
4. There are many possible
   answers.

Progress check 1

1. hill   till   bell   well
2. red: rack   pack
   yellow: neck   deck
   orange: lock   rock
   green: duck   suck
   blue: lick   sick
3. moon bee tree   pool
4. king   gong bung
5. **nd** words:
   bend pond mend
   nt words:
   went tint hunt
6. **br** words: brick   brag
   cr words: crick crag crop
   crack
   dr words: drag   drop
   pr words: prick prod prop
   tr words: trick trod track

Answers

Unit 7

1. hold cold fold gold sold
2. **lf** words: elf shelf golf
   lk words: sulk milk bulk silk
   lp words: help yelp
   lt words: belt bolt jolt melt felt
3. milk   cold   old
   elf   help   belt
4. belt   milk
   elf   help
   old   cold
5. jolt
   sulk
   told
   golf

Unit 8

1. stick stack sting stop stamp
2. stamp
   sting
   stick
   stack
   stop
3. **ast** words: fast   past   last
   est words: best   rest   vest
   ist words: fist   list   mist
   ost words: cost   lost
   ust words: must dust rust
4. **st** at the beginning:
   stiff, stab, stock, stand, stuck
   st at the end:
   pest, test, rust, past, fist

Unit 9

1. chin chick chimp cheese
   chips chair
   a. chick b. chimp c. cheese
   d. chin e. chair f. chips
2. **ch**at **ch**eck mu**ch** su**ch**
   chop ri**ch** **ch**ocolate **ch**urch
3. ship shell sheep shop shut
   hush wish crash cash fish
4. fish shell cash shop crash
5. check shut chill shed child
   shoot lunch dash blush pinch

Unit 10

1. a. bar b. far   c. car
   d. jar   e. tar
2. bark dark mark park shark
3. lark – spark;   barn – darn;
   car – far;   march – starch;
   farm – charm;   hard – card;
   dart – part
4. bark scarf sharp arch
5. carpet target darling
   market

Unit 11

1. may   sway
   day   pray
   say   play
   hay   stay
   bay   clay
   pay   tray
2. Friday   Tuesday
   Monday   Thursday
   Sunday   Wednesday
   Saturday

Unit 11

3. Sunday, Monday, Tuesday,
   Wednesday, Thursday,
   Friday, Saturday
4. tray clay hay play
5. day   say
   play   sway
   way   pray

Unit 12

1. b**ow**l b**a**th w**hen** **duck**ed
   sp**otter** **ra**ther eleph**ant**
   esc**ape**
2. cat dog goat seal
   camel badger
3. **pot**ato **car**rot **on**ion
   spr**out** cauli**flow**er **turn**ip
4. call pink band cluck
   bring farmer monkey
5. mat the he hat
   bet than an any
   (Many possible answers.)

Progress check 2

1. gold   milk   belt
2. red: fast   last
   yellow: best   vest
   blue: mist   fist
   green: must   dust
   orange: cost   lost
3. chick sheep chips shell
4. jars shark target farmer
5. real words: pay day way
   clay play tray sway
6. s**cat**ter **then** b**ox**ing gr**ape**
   s**kid**s sti**ffly** **moth**er **bee**n
   feel sel**fish** **bear**d

Record sheet

How easy did you find it?

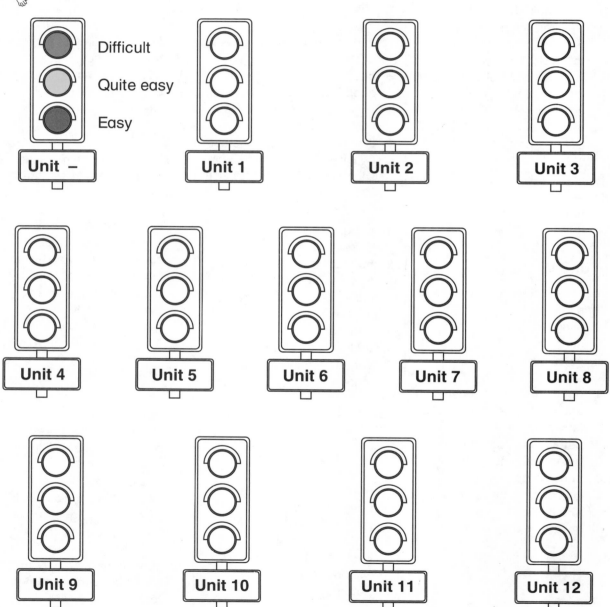

Difficult

Quite easy

Easy

Unit –

Unit 1

Unit 2

Unit 3

Unit 4

Unit 5

Unit 6

Unit 7

Unit 8

Unit 9

Unit 10

Unit 11

Unit 12